fun to make

Paper

Craft

illustrated by ANNA CURTI

Michael O'Mara Books Limited

Welcome to *Paper Craft*! My name is Andrew and this is my sister Julie. These two are our cousins, Michael and Claire. Tom and Anne are our friends. Together, we have created all the activities that you will find in this book.

You'll have great fun making these little 'masterpieces'. It's so easy! All you need is paper, card and cardboard, coloured pencils, sticky tape, glue, round-ended scissors and two or three other things that I'll tell you about as we go along. The little mouse in the margin shows you which are the special pull-out pages. Have fun!

CLAIRE   ANNE   TOM   JULIE   MICHAEL   ANDREW

THIS BOOK BELONGS TO

LET'S BUILD A TOWN FULL OF PEOPLE

Today, our teacher asked us to bring some special things into class: thin card, scissors and glue. It' really exciting . . . we are going to build a town with houses, a supermarket, trees and people!

1. First you need to copy a picture. Take a sheet of tracing paper and put it over the picture you want to copy. Now draw over the picture. It is very easy because the tracing paper is see-through.

5. Use scissors to carefully cut out the drawing. If you find it difficult, ask an adult to help you.

3. You can also make a copy of a picture by putting your tracing paper on a glass table with a light underneath, and drawing round the outline you see.

2. Stick the tracing paper on to a window with sticky tape. Put a piece of thin card over the tracing paper and draw round the outline you can see showing through.

6. Fold round the tabs at the side and tape them together as shown. Your little figure can now stand up. To make it stronger, you could use staples to hold the tabs together.

4. Now colour in the drawing using coloured pencils, felt-tip pens or even paint.

Each of the stand-up figures can be used as a finger-puppet, or can be placed outside the buildings you will make next.

you want to use the figure as a uppet, slip it over two fingers.

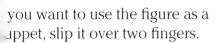

LITTLE GIRL WITH HER DOG

POLICEMAN

JOGGER

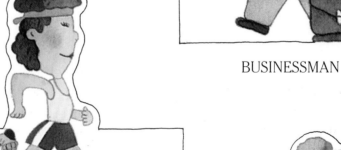

BUSINESSMAN

ICE-CREAM SELLER

OLD LADY

7

Houses

My sister Julie is in the same class as me at school. So are my cousins, Michael and Claire, my friends Tom and Anne, and lots of other friends. We had lots of fun with our finger-puppets, the houses and all the other things that we made. You can make the same things using the next few pages of this book.

DOG

CAT

MOUSE

LET'S BUILD A BLOCK OF FLATS

To make this building and those that come later in the book, carefully detach the page along the dotted line. Now, cut around the pictures, fold them along the black lines and glue the white tabs together as shown.

Cut out the roof and put it on top of the building. You can choose a roof with a garden or a roof with a swimming pool. Or you could simply place it next to the block of flats. Look how lovely it is!

TREE

ROOF WITH SWIMMING POOL

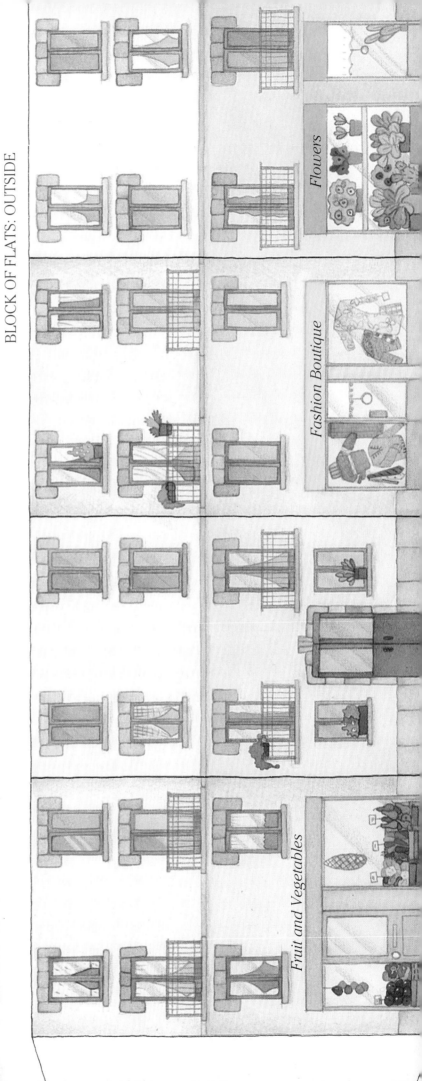

Flowers

Fashion Boutique

Fruit and Vegetables

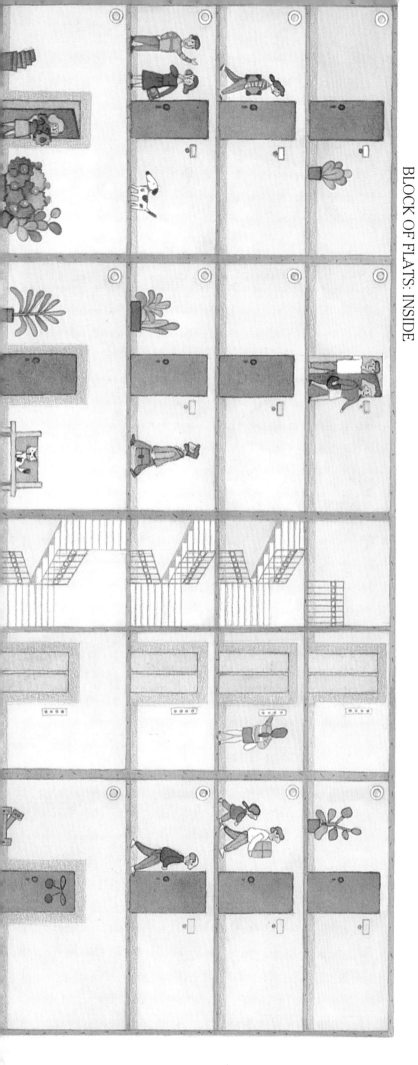

There are lots of flats in this block. That's why you see a number of doors on each floor. To go up or down a floor, people take the lift or use the stairs. There are shops on the ground floor.

TREE

ROOF WITH GARDEN

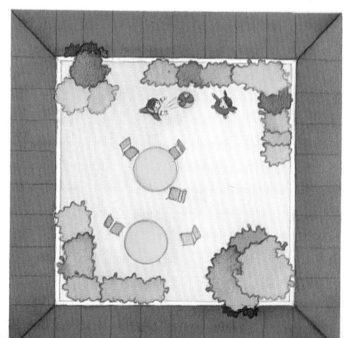

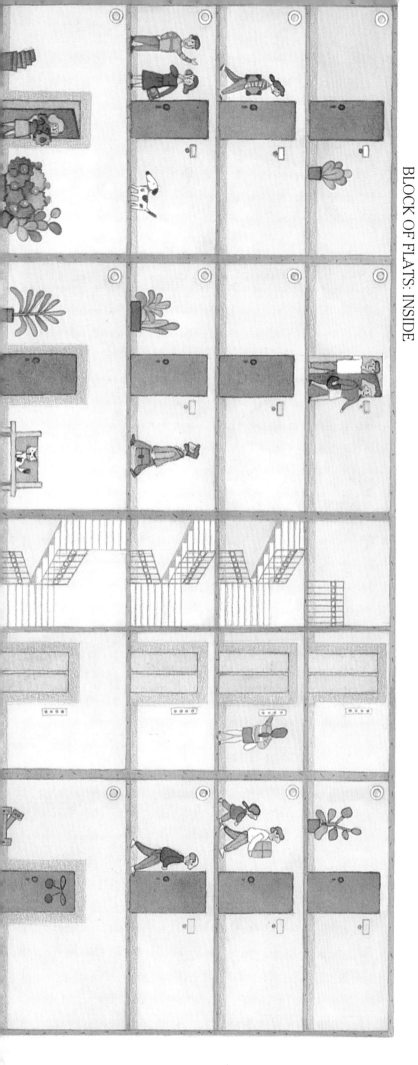

LET'S BUILD AN OFFICE BLOCK

Pull this page out! Now you can cut around and build an office block. Don't forget to put the roof on top!

Cut out the tree, and fix the white tabs together so it stands up.

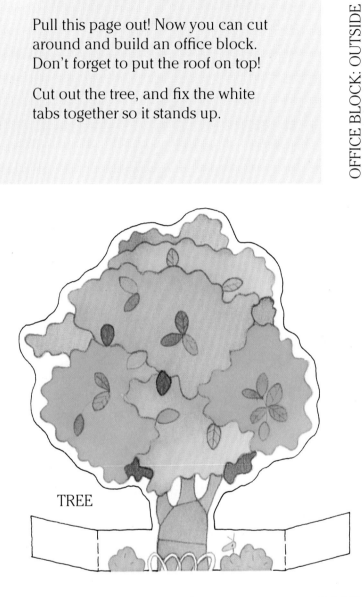

TREE

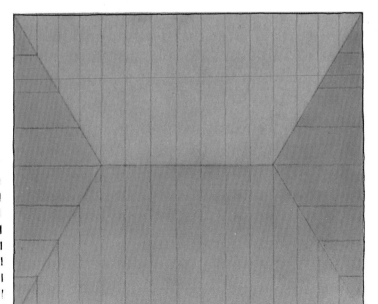

ROOF

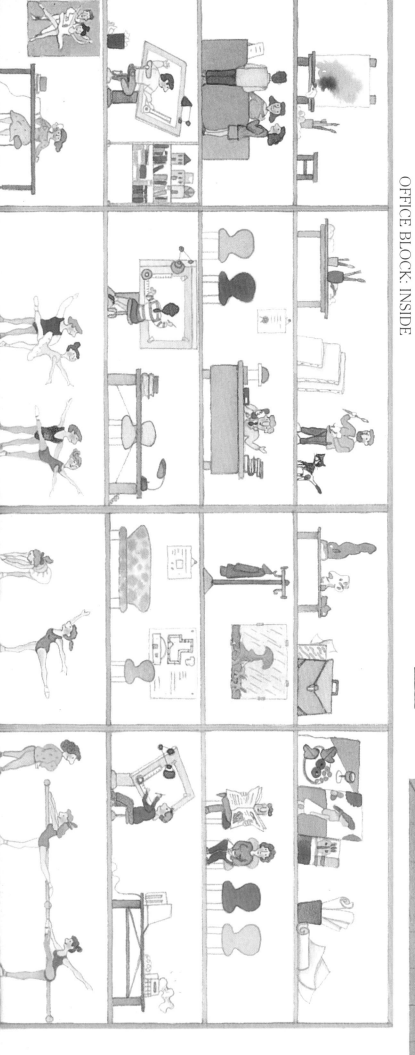

In a building like this, each floor can have a different function. This elegant block contains a dance school, an architect's office, a lawyer's practice, and a studio used by a painter and sculptor.

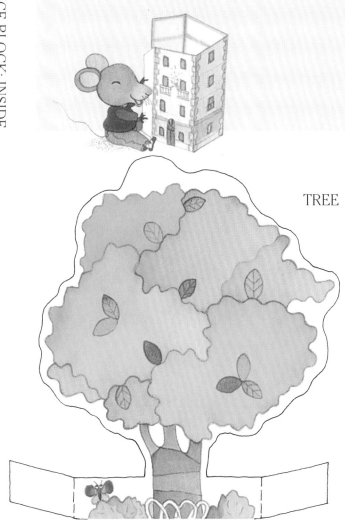

TREE

ROOF

LET'S BUILD A HOUSE

Now I'm going to show you an easy way to pull out this page. Take a ruler and put it along the dotted line. Fold the page and pull.

Now that you know what to do, let's build this house!

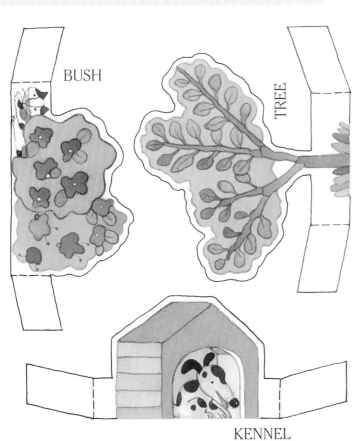

BUSH

TREE

KENNEL

ROOF

8

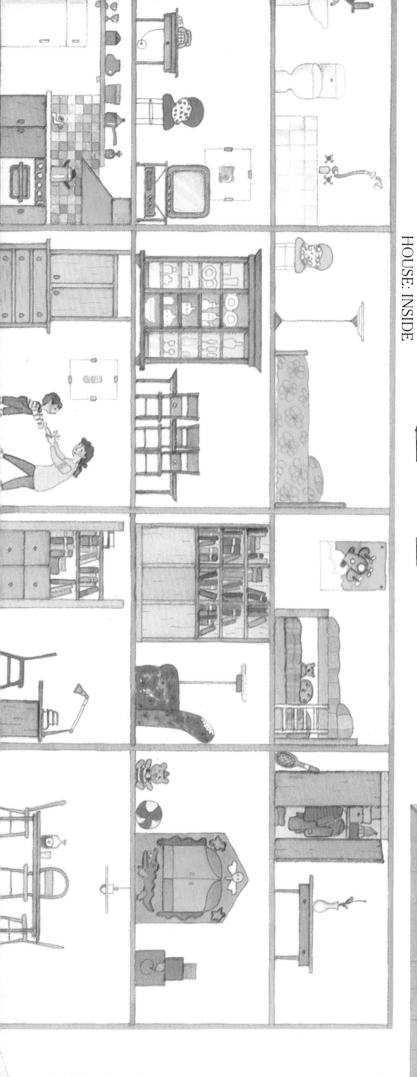

It's lovely to live in a house with a garden. There is often more space in a house in the country than in a flat in a city. Look! This house even has a playroom! And the dog has a little house of his own called a kennel!

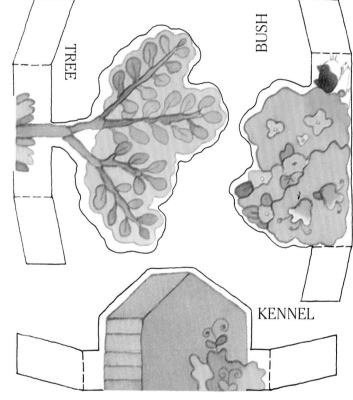

TREE

BUSH

KENNEL

ROOF

LET'S BUILD A SUPERMARKET

A town is not complete without a supermarket! Here it is. Cut it out, fold it, and glue the tabs.

You can either put the roof on top, or put it next to the supermarket. It has a car park on one side and a playpark on the other.

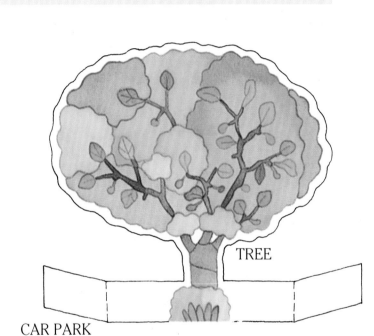

TREE

CAR PARK

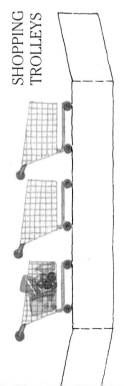

SHOPPING TROLLEYS

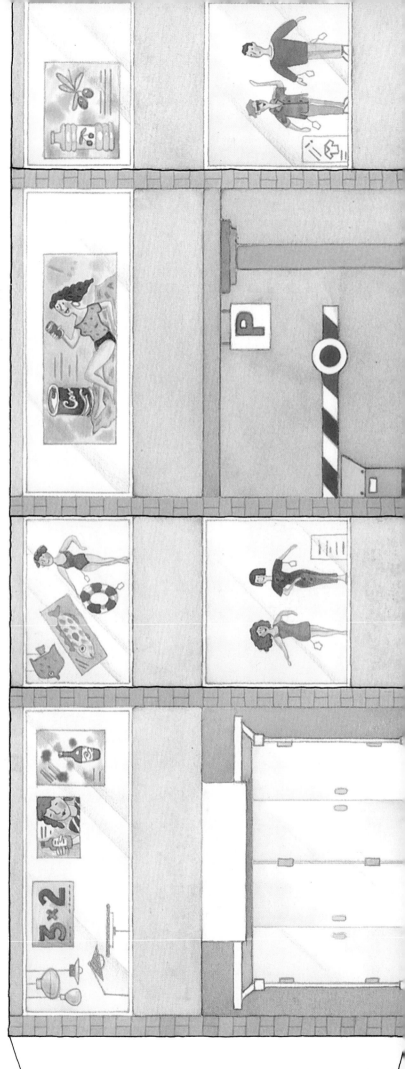

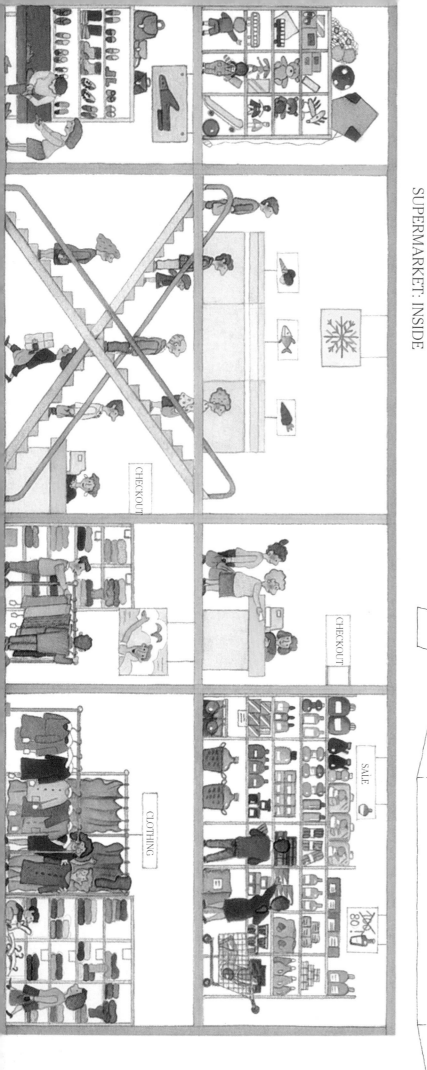

SUPERMARKET: INSIDE

CHECKOUT

CHECKOUT

CLOTHING

SALE

The supermarket is a good place to do your shopping. You can find everything you need there: food, clothes, books, toys . . . Choose the things that you want to buy, put them in the trolley, and pay at the checkout.

TREE

PLAYPARK

SHOPPING TROLLEYS

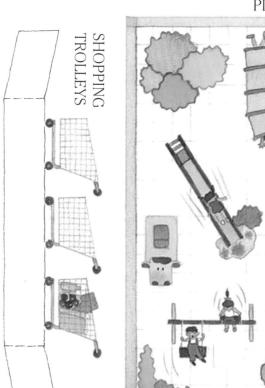

ANIMAL PLACE-MARKERS

Today, I have invited some friends for lunch. So that everyone knows where to sit, I have made them place-markers with their names on (there is even one for me!) and I have put one next to each plate.

1. To make the place-markers, copy the pig drawing below. Follow the tracing instructions on page 6. Then draw them on to card.
2. Fold the card along the dotted line. Colour in the drawing and write a name on the inside of the card.

The place-markers show funny animals: you can have fun deciding which animal each of your friends should be! They can take them home after the meal.

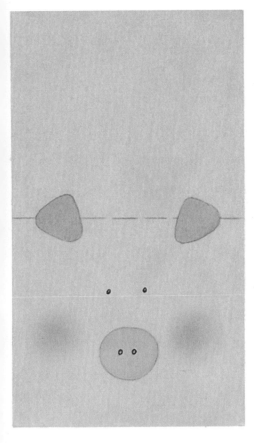

PIG

CAT

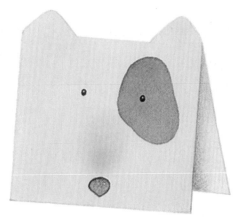

DOG

ELEPHANT

CAT CARDS

Our teacher helped us make a lovely card for Mother's Day in the shape of a family of cats: mother cat, father cat and baby cat. The teacher told us that our mothers would be delighted to receive cards made specially for them!

1. Copy these drawings, but this time draw on both sides of the card.

2. Colour the cats in, cut them out, fold them, and then write a special message to your mother on the inside.

CAT FAMILY: FRONT

You can also make cards with other members of the cat family: lions, tigers or leopards.

CAT FAMILY: BACK

FOLDED CARD

TRACE
(see page 6)

FOLD

CUT OUT

GIVE

FOLDED ANIMAL CARDS

You only need a piece of paper and a pencil to be able to write a letter. But if you want the letter to be unusual, you need to use a little imagination. I'm going to show you how to make a letter that you can give to your brother or your father as a birthday card . . .

1. Copy this drawing on to card, colour it in and cut it out.

2. Fold it along the dotted line and write in the middle section.

OWL

Can you think of other ideas? Can you draw an elephant, a penguin or a walrus?

GORILLA

GONE FISHING

Today our teacher talked to us about the animals that live in the sea, in rivers and in lakes. Then she taught us how to make creatures that float, and how to make a fishing rod.

1. To make the whale and the other animals on this page, draw the outline of the animal on to card, colour it in and cut it out.

2. Ask and adult to cut a cork in half lengthways and to make a little slot in it to glue the animal in. Attach a paper clip on the back of the picture with a piece of sticky tape, as shown.

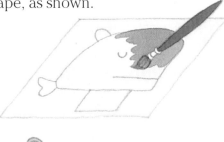

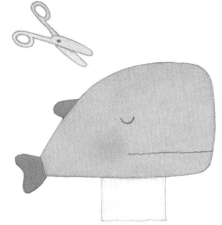

WHALE: BACK

WHALE: FRONT

3. To make the fishing rod, take a small stick and tie a piece of string on to it. Attach an opened paper clip to the other end of the string.

FISHING ROD

SHARK

SQUID

DOLPHIN

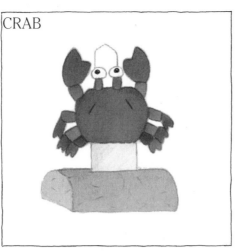

To play the fishing game, we put our floating creatures into a paddling pool full of water. We tried to catch them with a fishing rod. Fishing is much more difficult than we thought, because the creatures move around in the water!
Anne won: she caught the most creatures!

21

CHILDREN OF THE WORLD

There are lots of children around the world. We are all similar but each one of us is unique. Children are all different because they have different faces, different hair and different personalities . . .

1. To make Paul, trace these two faces on to card, as shown on page 6.

2. Colour them in and cut them out.

MY NAME IS PAUL
I LAUGH AND I CRY

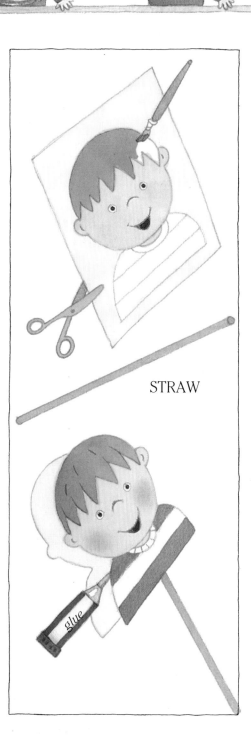

STRAW

3. Now that you have cut out the two pictures of Paul's face, stick them together, back to back, with a drinking straw or a small round stick in between.

4. Twirl the stick round between your hands.

All children are alike: we laugh, we cry, we sleep . . .
But we are all different – there is only one you! That's what our teacher told us at school today!

Then we made children from different parts the world, with two faces and twirled them round in our hands.

MY NAME IS TAI AND I LIVE IN JAPAN

MY NAME IS TOM AND I LIVE IN AMERICA

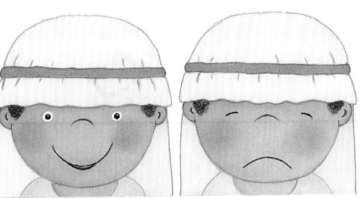

MY NAME IS EMIR AND I LIVE IN EGYPT

MY NAME IS QUEQUA AND I LIVE IN THE ANDES

MY NAME IS MARY AND I LIVE IN IRELAND

MY NAME IS MOONFEATHER, I LIVE IN NORTH AMERICA

Here are some other characters with two faces:

SUN AND MOON

SMILING STAR AND SLEEPING STAR

Our teacher showed us on a map of the world where the children that we made live. Then each child in the class showed everyone their 'children with two faces' and told us who they were. For example, Michael said 'My name is Emir, and I live in Egypt'. We saw the children laugh and cry, and we saw them awake and asleep. We had lots of fun!

MERRY-GO-ROUND

Now let's make a merry-go-round. Pull the page out along the dotted line. Cut around the circle and cut into the centre. Glue the white tab at the back to make a cone – this is the roof of the merry-go-round.

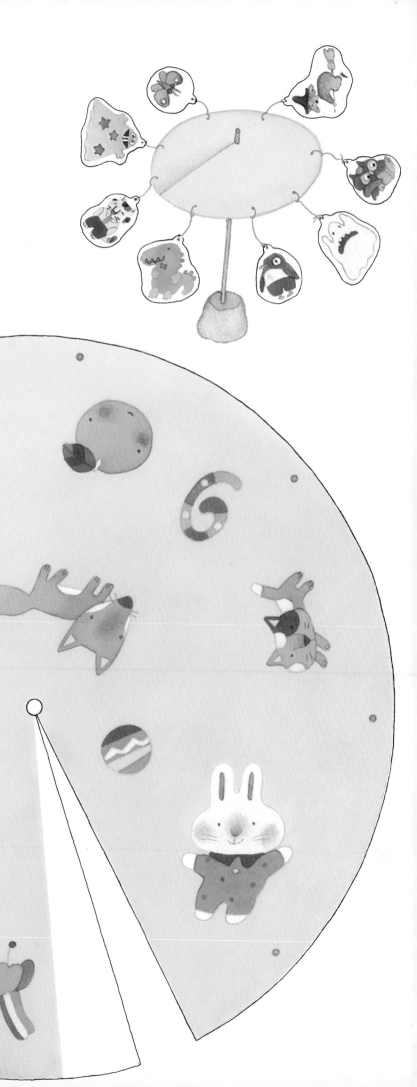

On the next page you will find eight characters for the merry-go-round. Cut them out. Use a large needle to thread each one on a piece of wool and attach them to the roof of the merry-go-round at the yellow dots, as shown. Make sure your merry-go-round balances properly. Now all you need is a small round stick to glue into the centre of the merry-go-round. Twirl the stick round between your hands to make the merry-go-round spin round. When you have finished playing with it, stick it into a piece of modelling clay, where it will stand safely until you next play with it.

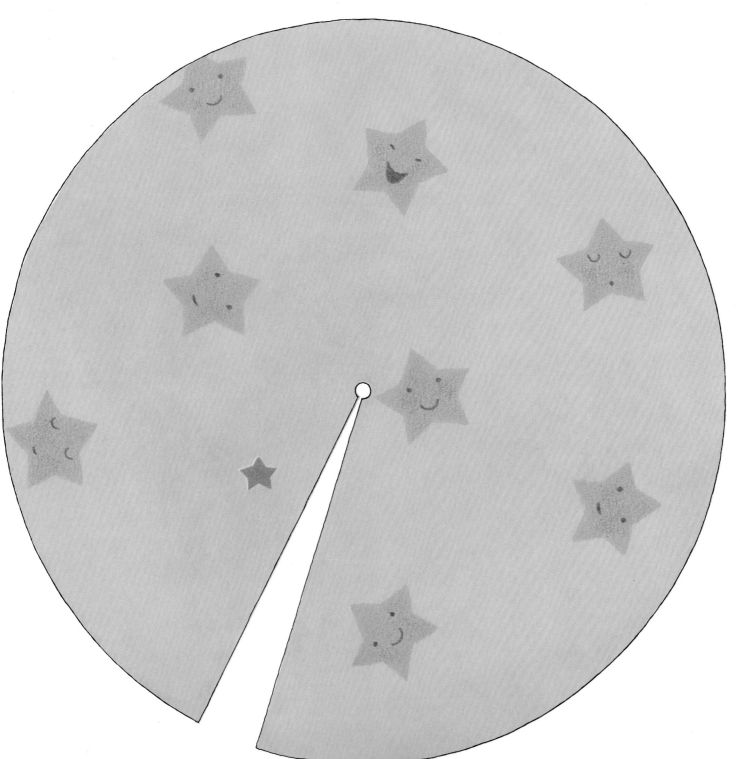

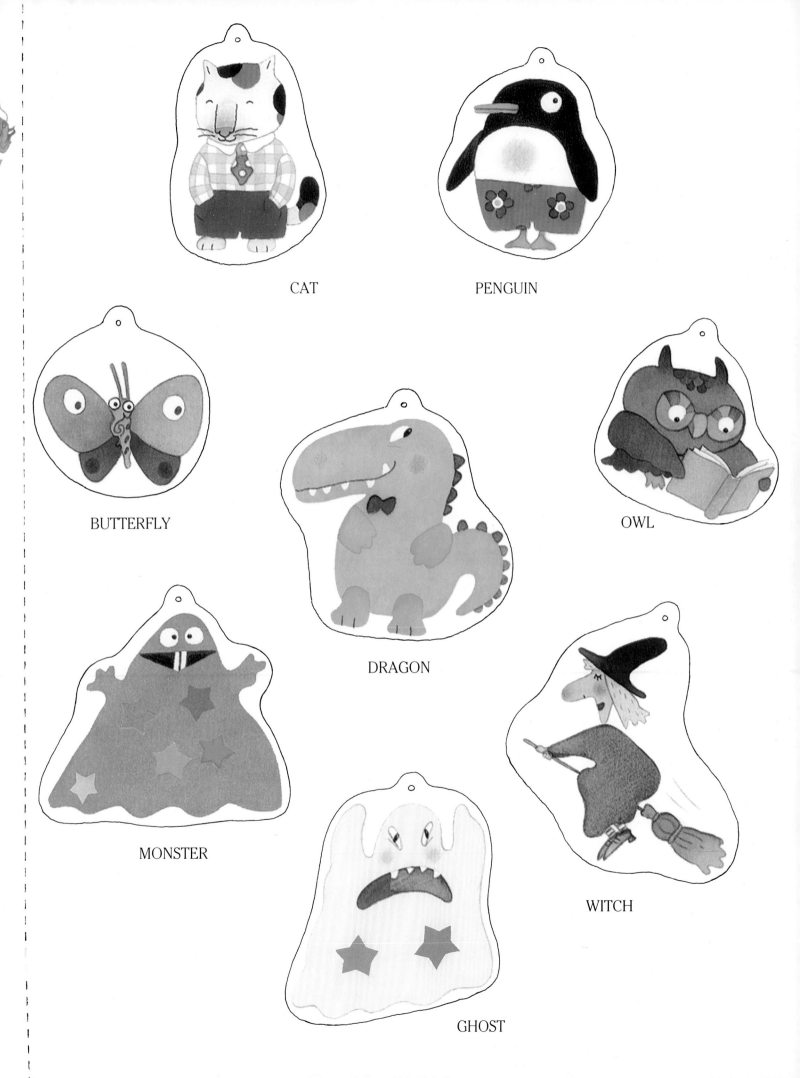

CAT

PENGUIN

BUTTERFLY

DRAGON

OWL

MONSTER

GHOST

WITCH

PENGUIN

CAT

OWL

DRAGON

BUTTERFLY

WITCH

MONSTER

GHOST

MAGIC SPINNERS

This is a very simple game. I call it Magic Spinners because, when you spin the two strings you have attached to the circles on this page, it will look as though the pictures on them are moving. What is outside will look as though it is inside, what is underneath will look as though it is on top. So the little bird will look as though he is inside his cage, the fish will be in their bowl, the chicken will be sitting on its egg, and the cat will sit on the cushion . . .

BIRD/CAGE

FLOWER/VASE

SUN/WINDOW

FISH/BOWL

1. Remove this page along the dotted line. Cut out the circles. Using a large needle, thread one piece of string through each of the holes marked at the sides of the circles.

2. Hold the two pieces of string and swing them round in one direction until they are twisted. Now pull the two strings and watch how quickly the card circle spins round. Isn't it easy? And it looks like magic!

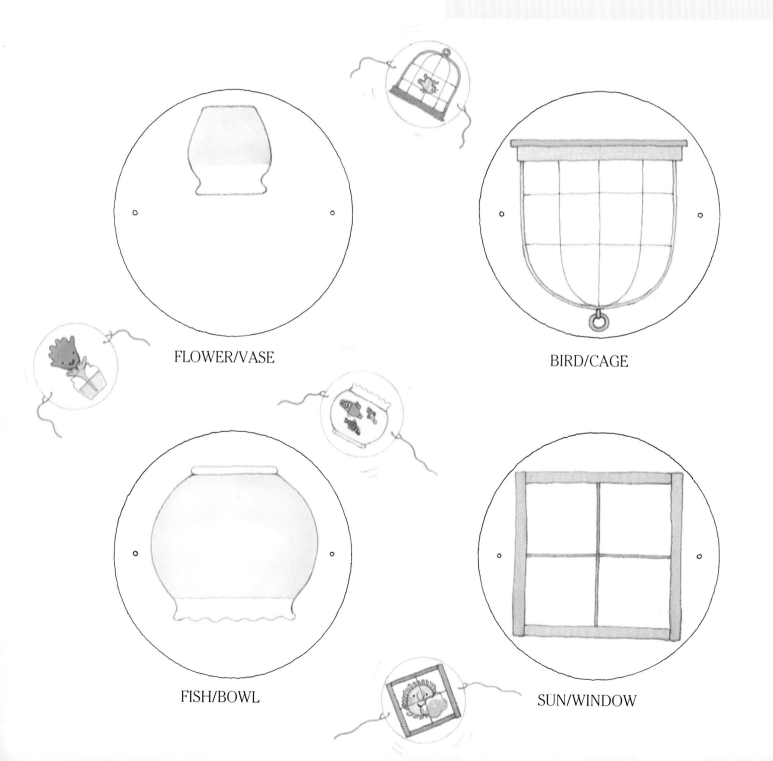

FLOWER/VASE

BIRD/CAGE

FISH/BOWL

SUN/WINDOW

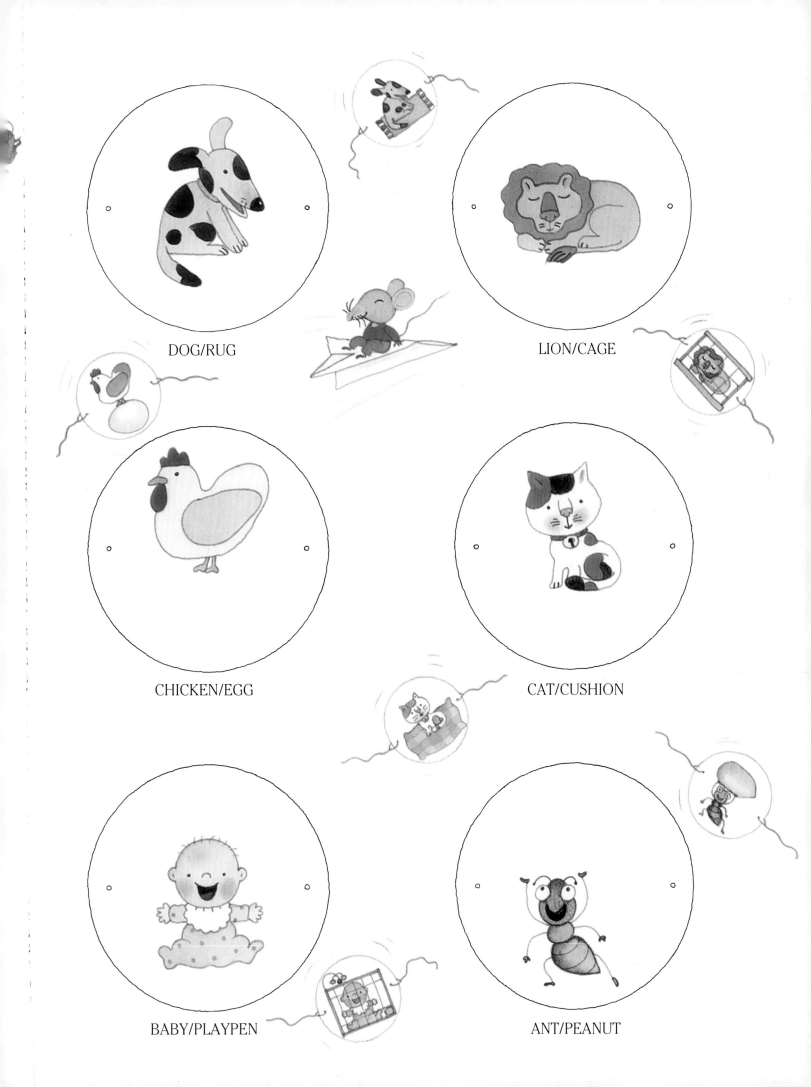

DOG/RUG

LION/CAGE

CHICKEN/EGG

CAT/CUSHION

BABY/PLAYPEN

ANT/PEANUT

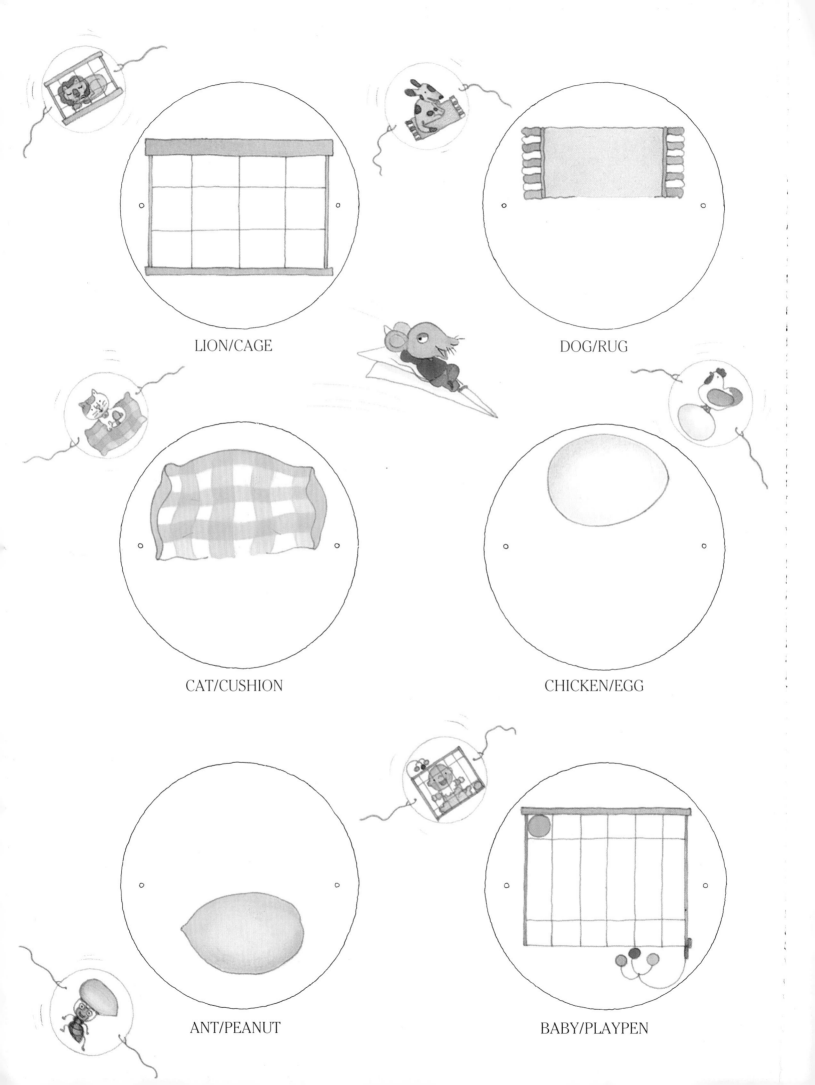

LION/CAGE

DOG/RUG

CAT/CUSHION

CHICKEN/EGG

ANT/PEANUT

BABY/PLAYPEN

THE HUNGRY MONSTER

Have you ever played ball with a hungry monster? No? Well, let's try! I will show you how to make your monster.

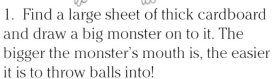

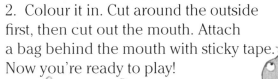

1. Find a large sheet of thick cardboard and draw a big monster on to it. The bigger the monster's mouth is, the easier it is to throw balls into!

2. Colour it in. Cut around the outside first, then cut out the mouth. Attach a bag behind the mouth with sticky tape. Now you're ready to play!

THE TWISTING SNAKE

Do you want to play a trick on your friends? Make a snake that moves all by itself. You need to use thin paper. The thinner the paper, the better the effect will be.

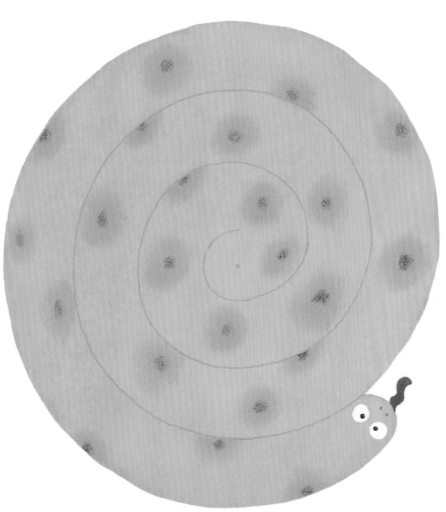

Our teacher explained to us that if we put a piece of paper on a hot radiator, it will float upwards. This is because warm air is lighter than cold air, so the warm air rises. This is how we make the snake move all by itself.

1. To make the snake, trace the picture on this page on to a thin piece of paper (see page 6). Colour it in.

2. Carefully cut along the solid line.
3. Using a large needle, thread a piece of string through the snake's tail.
4. Hold it over a radiator. Look, the snake moves by itself!

You can make lots of snakes and hang them from the ceiling.

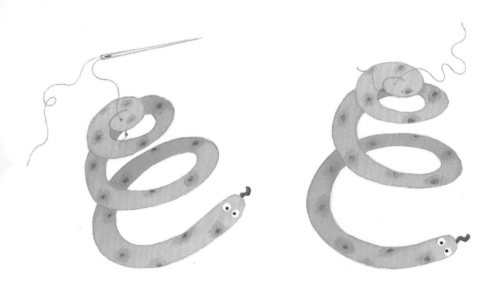

MARBLE CARTS

Here is another game that is simple to make and fun to play: a race between robots and monsters. You need marbles, thick card and a sloped surface. Ready, steady . . . go!

MONSTER 1: BACK

MONSTER 1: FRONT

1. Trace Monster 1 on to some thick card. As you can see, the monster has a front and back.

2. Colour the card on both sides and cut out the monster. Put a blob of glue between the monster's two 'arms' to join them together.

glue

3. Place a marble between its arms.

ROBOT 1

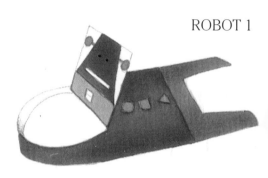

4. Make other monsters or robots in the same way. Make a smooth, sloped surface with a plank of wood propped up on some books. Put a marble between the arms of each monster . . . and you're ready to race! One, two, three . . . go!

ROBOT 2

ROBOT 3

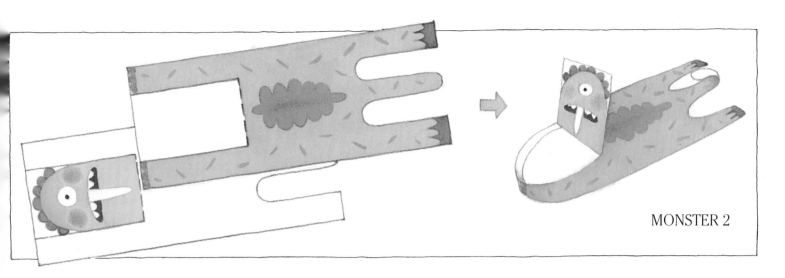

MONSTER 2

MONSTER 3

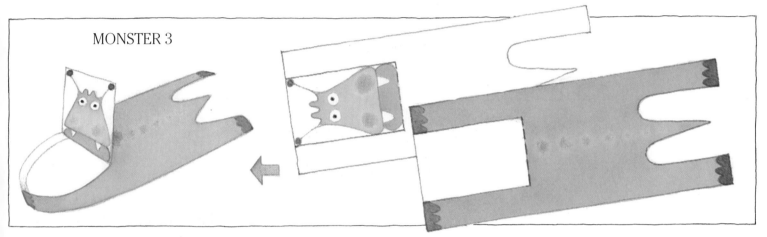

First published in Great Britain in 1998
by Michael O'Mara Books Limited,
9 Lion Yard, Tremadoc Road,
London SW4 7NQ
Copyright © 1996 Happy Books, Milan
Originally published in Italy by Happy Books in 1996.
All rights reserved including the right of reproduction
in whole or in part in any form.
Illustrations by Anna Curti
Translation and editing by Book Creation Services, London
Cover design by Reo Design Partnership.
English series editor: Helen Burnford
Printed and bound in Italy
ISBN 1–85479–381–0

Have fun!